CW00410534

Intermittent Fasting Guide

Intermittent Fasting. A healthy and effective guide to loss fat with intermittent fasting

Table of Contents

7

BREAKFAST

Classic Spanakopita Frittata

Preparation Time: 10 minutes

Cooking Time: 3-4 hours

Servings: 8

Ingredients:

- 12 eggs, beaten
- ½ cup feta cheese
- cup heavy whipping cream
- cups spinach, chopped
- teaspoons garlic, minced
- From the cupboard:
- 1 tablespoon extra-virgin olive oil

Directions:

1. Grease the bottom of the slow cooker, put with the olive oil lightly.
2. Stir together the beaten eggs, feta cheese, heavy cream, spinach, and garlic until well combined.
3. Slowly pour the mixture into the slow cooker. Cook covered on LOW for 3 to 4 hours, or until a knife inserted in the center comes out clean.
4. Take off from the slow cooker and cool for about 3 minutes before slicing.

Nutrition: Calories: 254 Fat: 22.3g Protein: 11.1g Net carbs: 2.1g Fiber: 0g Cholesterol: 364mg

Sausage Stuffed Bell Peppers

Preparation Time: 15 minutes

Cooking Time: 4-5 hours

Servings: 4

Ingredients:

- cup breakfast sausage, crumbled
- 4 bell peppers, seedless and cut the top
- ½ cup coconut milk
- 6 eggs
- 1 cup cheddar cheese, shredded
- From the cupboard:
- 1 tablespoon extra-virgin olive oil
- ½ teaspoon freshly ground black pepper

Directions:

1. Add the coconut milk, eggs, and black pepper in a medium bowl, whisking until smooth. Set aside.
2. Line your slow cooker insert with aluminum foil. Grease the aluminum foil with 1 tablespoon olive oil.
3. Evenly stuff four bell peppers with the crumbled sausage, and spoon the egg mixture into the peppers.
4. Arrange the stuffed peppers in the slow cooker. Sprinkle the cheese on top.
5. Cook covered on LOW for 4 t0 5 hours, or until the peppers are browned and the eggs are completely set.

6. Divide in 4 serving plates and serve warm.

Nutrition: Calories: 459 Fat: 36.3g Protein: 25.2g Net carbs: 7.9g Fiber: 3g Cholesterol: 376mg

Intermittent Tacos with Guacamole and Bacon

Preparation Time: 5 minutes

Cooking Time: 10 minutes

Servings: 2

Ingredients:

- 1/4 cup organic romaine lettuce (chopped)
- 3 tablespoons organic sweet potatoes (diced and cooked)
- tablespoon Brain Octane Oil
- 1 tablespoon ghee (grass-fed)
- pieces eggs (pasture-raised)
- 1 piece medium avocado (organic)
- slices pastured bacon (cooked)
- 1/4 teaspoon Himalayan pink salt
- organic micro cilantro (for garnish)

Directions:

1. In a skillet over medium heat, heat up the ghee.
2. Get an egg. Crack the egg in the middle of the skillet. Poke the egg yolk.
3. Let the egg cook until solid for about 2 minutes per side. Transfer the cooked egg onto a plate lined with paper towels to absorb the excess oil.
4. Cook the other egg in a similar way. The 2 cooked eggs will serve as the taco shells.

5. In a mixing bowl, put in the avocado, pink salt, and octane oil. Mash the avocado and mix well.
6. Equally divide the avocado mixture into 2 portions. Spread each avocado mixture onto each egg taco.
7. Arrange the romaine lettuce on top of each taco shell.
8. Put a bacon slice on each taco. Top each taco with the cooked sweet potatoes.
9. Garnish the tacos with micro cilantro and sprinkle some pink salt for added taste.
10. Fold each taco in half. Serve.

Nutrition: Calories: 387 Carbs: 9 g Fats: 35 g Proteins: 11 g Fiber: 5 g

Zucchini Pancakes

Preparation Time: 5 minutes

Cooking Time: 10 minutes

Servings: 3

Ingredients:

- 1,5 oz. zucchini
- ½ cup almond flour
- 2 tbsp. coconut flour
- oz. full-fat milk
- eggs
- ½ tsp baking powder
- 1 tsp cinnamon
- 1 tbsp. ghee butter
- Salt and erythritol to taste

Directions:

1. Grate the zucchini, season with salt and place into a sieve to drain
2. .Put into a blender, add other ingredients, pulse well
3. Heat then melt the butter in a pan in medium heat
4. Form the pancakes and put into the skillet
5. Close the lid and cook 3 minutes each side

Nutrition: Carbs: 0 7 g Fats: 7 g Protein: 7 5 g Calories: 130

Shrimp Omelet

Preparation Time: 5 minutes

Cooking Time: 15 minutes

Servings: 4

Ingredients:

- 10 oz. boiled shrimps
- 12 eggs
- 4 tbsp. ghee butter
- 4 garlic cloves
- cup intermittent mayo
- fresh red chili peppers
- tbsp. olive oil
- 1 tsp cumin powder

Directions:

1. Mince the garlic cloves and chili pepper
2. In a bowl, blend the shrimps with the mayo, olive oil, minced chili pepper, cumin, minced garlic, salt, and pepper. Set aside for a while
3. In the other bowl, whisk the eggs then add salt and pepper
4. Heat the ghee butter in the skillet, add eggs and shrimp mixture
5. Cook for 5-6 minutes, serve hot

Nutrition: Carbs: 4 g Fat: 82 g Protein: 27 g Calories: 855

Cauliflower Patties

Preparation Time: 11 minutes

Cooking Time: 15 minutes

Servings: 2

Ingredients:

- 10 oz. cauliflower
- tbsp. yeast
- 2/3 cup almond flour
- ½ tsp cumin powder
- ½ tsp paprika
- eggs
- tbsp. ghee butter
- Salt and pepper to taste

Directions:

1. Divide the cauliflower into florets, put them in a pot and boil for 8-10 min
2. Remove to a plate and let it rest for 3-4 min
3. Meanwhile, in a bowl combine the eggs, paprika, cumin, yeast, pepper, salt
4. Put the cauliflower in a blender and pulse till even
5. Add the cauliflower to the bowl with other mixed ingredients, mix well and form the patties
6. Heat the ghee butter in a skillet over medium heat, cook the patties for 3-5 min per side

Nutrition: Carbs: 5 g Fat: 23 g Protein: 6 g Calories: 235

Spinach Sandwich

Preparation Time: 7 minutes

Cooking Time: 8 minutes

Servings: 1

Ingredients:

- ½ avocado
- 2 oz. spinach
- oz. cheddar cheese
- 1 tbsp. coconut oil
- cherry tomatoes
- Salt and pepper to taste

Directions:

1. Mince the spinach; place it in a small plate. Make a round cutlet out of it
2. Grate the cheese, slice the avocado and cut tomatoes in halves
3. Sprinkle the oil on the leaves, place the grated cheddar cheese, avocado, and tomato on top of it. Season with salt and pepper

Nutrition: Carbs: 4 g Fat: 43 g Protein: 4 g Calories: 419 kcal

Fried Eggs with Bacon

Preparation Time: 5 minutes

Cooking Time: 10 minutes

Servings: 4

Ingredients:

- 8 medium eggs
- 5 oz. bacon
- 2 medium tomatoes
- tsp chopped parsley
- 1 tbsp. ghee butter
- Salt to taste

Directions:

1. Heat the ghee butter in a skillet over medium-high heat
2. Slice the bacon and fry it until crispy for 3-4 minutes, then set aside on a paper towel
3. Meanwhile, cut the tomatoes in small cubes
4. Crack the eggs in the same skillet, add tomatoes, season with salt and cook till the desired readiness
5. Top with the bacon and parsley. Serve hot

Nutrition: Carbs: 1 g Fat: 22 g Protein: 15 g Calories: 273

LUNCH RECIPES

Chicken Pizzaiola

Preparation Time: 10 minutes

Cooking Time: 20 minutes

Servings: 3

Ingredients:

- 3 chicken breasts

- 1 tray with ham

- 1 cup pasta sauce

- 1 and ½ cups grated cheese

- 1 Pinch of salt and pepper

- 2 Tbsps. olive oil

Directions:

1. Preheat the oven to 290 °F

2. Place the 3 chicken breasts on a sheet of parchment paper directly on the plate of your oven.

3. Slice the breasts partially and garnish with sauce, ham, and cheese.

4. Cover with grated cheese, season with salt and pepper and drizzle with oil.

5. Bake in a hot oven for 20 minutes

6. Once ready, divide the 2 chicken breasts between three containers

7. Seal the containers very well and store it in the refrigerator for 3 days

Nutrition: Calories: 453 Fat: 34.8 g Carbs: 8.9 g Protein 26g Sugar: 1.5 g

Beef Stroganoff with Protein Noodles

Preparation Time: 14 minutes

Cooking Time: 29 min

Servings: 1

Ingredients:

- 2 oz. Barilla Protein Farfalle Pasta

- ½ cup fresh sliced mushrooms

- 2 Tbsp of chopped onion

- 1 T butter

- dash of black pepper

- 6 oz. steak, sliced thinly

- 1 T tomato paste

- ¼ tsp of Dijon mustard

- ½ cup beef broth

- ½ small container plain Greek yogurt

Directions:

1. Cook the pasta in water.

2. Place the butter in a Teflon skillet.

3. Next add in the onions, and mushrooms, cook until onions are shiny and water is gone.

4. Add the beef and brown well.

5. Stir in remaining ingredients except the pasta and yogurt.

6. Cook this until the beef is done, approximately 9 minutes.

7. Drain the pasta.

8. If the sauce is too thin, add 1 tsp low carb flax meal and boil to thicken.

9. Turn back down to low. Then add the yogurt to the sauce.

10. Serve the stroganoff over the pasta.

Nutrition: Calories: 559 Total Fat: 23g; Protein: 55g Total Carbs: 4g Dietary Fiber: 13g Sugar: 2g Sodium: 957mg

Beefy Tostadas

Preparation Time: 4 minute

Cooking Time: 9 minutes

Servings: 2

Ingredients:

- ¼ pound ground sirloin

- ¼ cup onions, minced

- 1 tsp garlic, minced

- 1 T olive oil

- ½ cup chopped green, red, and yellow peppers

- ½ cup cheddar cheese, mild or sharp, hand-shredded

- 2 Tortilla factory low-carb tortillas

- 2 T butter

- 1 c Greek yogurt, plain

- 2 T salsa Verde

Directions:

1. Brown the tortillas in the butter. Place on a warm plate.

2. Cook the sirloin, onions, garlic, peppers in the olive oil.

3. Place on the tortillas.

4. Top with the cheese.

5. Add the Greek yogurt.

6. Drizzle with the salsa.

Nutrition: Calories: 735 Total Fat: 48g Protein: 66g Total Carbs: 18g Dietary Fiber: 8g Sugar: 0g Sodium: 708mg

Bratwurst German Dinner

Preparation Time: 4 minutes

Cooking Time: 19 minutes

Servings:

Ingredients:

- 1 Bratwurst sausage

- ½ cup sliced onion

- ½ cup sauerkraut, this includes the liquid

- 1 tsp olive oil

- Sprinkle of black pepper

Directions:

1. Cook the bratwurst and the onion in the olive oil, in a coated skillet.

2. Remove the bratwurst to a plate.

3. Place the sauerkraut into the skillet and cook 3 min.

4. Add the bratwurst and onion back to warm and mingle the flavors.

5. Sprinkle with black pepper and serve.

Nutrition: Calories: 332 Total Fat: 26g Protein: 15g Total Carbs: 8g Dietary Fiber: 9g Sugar: 4g Sodium: 1188mg

Cajun Blackened Fish with Cauliflower Salad

Preparation Time: 9 minutes

Cooking Time: 9 minutes

Servings: 1

Ingredients:

- 1 cup chopped cauliflower
- 1 tsp red pepper flakes
- 1 T Italian seasonings
- 1 T garlic, minced
- 6 oz. tilapia
- 1 cup English cucumber, chopped with peel
- 2 T olive oil
- 1 sprig dill, chopped
- 1 Sweetener packet
- 3 T lime juice
- 2 T Cajun blackened seasoning

Directions:

1. Mix the seasonings, except the Cajun blackened seasoning, into one bowl.

2. Add 1 T olive oil.

3. Emulsify or whip.

4. Pour the dressing over the cauliflower and cucumber.

5. Brush the fish with the olive oil on both sides.

6. Pour the other 1 T oil into a coated skillet.

7. Press the Cajun seasoning onto both sides of the fish.

8. Cook the fish in the olive oil 3 minutes per side.

9. Plate and serve.

Nutrition: Calories: 530 Total Fat: 33.5g Protein: 32g Total Carbs: 5.5g Dietary Fiber: 4g Sugar: 3g Sodium: 80mg

Chicken Parmesan over Protein Pasta

Preparation Time: 9 minutes

Cooking Time: 14 minutes

Servings: 2

Ingredients:

- 1 dash black pepper

- ½ tsp Italian spice mix

- 8 oz. Protein Plus Spaghetti

- ½ hand-shredded Parmesan

- 1 diced zucchini squash

- 1 ½ cups marinara sauce, any brand

- 24 oz. boneless thin chicken cutlets

- 2 T olive oil

- ½ cup grated Mozzarella cheese

- Water, for boiling the pasta

Directions:

1. Boil the pasta with the zucchini in the water.

2. Mix the Italian spices and ¼ cup Parmesan cheese and place in a shallow dish.

3. Brush the chicken pieces with olive oil and press into spice and cheese to coat.

4. Place in skillet with the oil and cook until done.

5. Add the marinara sauce to the skillet to warm, cover the chicken if you desire.

6. Drain the pasta and zucchini, place on plates.

7. Top the chicken with the mozzarella and remaining Parmesan cheese.

8. Place sauce, chicken, and cheese onto spaghetti and serve.

Nutrition: Calories: 372 Total Fat: 18g Protein: 56g Total Carbs: 7 g Dietary Fiber: 2g Sugar: 6g Sodium: 1335mg

Chicken Chow Mein Stir Fry

Preparation Time: 9 minutes

Cooking Time: 14 minutes

Servings: 4

Ingredients:

- 1/2 cup sliced onion
- 2 T Oil, sesame garlic flavored
- 4 cups shredded Bok-Choy
- 1 c Sugar Snap Peas
- 1 cup fresh bean sprouts
- 3 stalks Celery, chopped
- 1 1/2 tsp minced Garlic
- 1 packet Splenda
- 1 cup Broth, chicken
- 2 T Soy Sauce
- 1 T ginger, freshly minced
- 1 tsp cornstarch
- 4 boneless Chicken Breasts, cooked/sliced thinly

Directions:

1. Place the bok-choy, peas, celery in a skillet with 1 T garlic oil.

2. Stir fry until bok-choy is softened to liking.

3. Add remaining ingredients except the cornstarch.

4. If too thin, stir cornstarch into ½ cup cold water. When smooth pour into skillet.

5. Bring cornstarch and chow mein to a one-minute boil. Turn off the heat source.

6. Stir sauce then for wait 4 minutes to serve, after the chow mein has thickened.

Nutrition: Calories: 368 Total Fat: 18g Protein: 42g Total Carbs: 12g Dietary Fiber: 16g Sugar: 6g Sodium: 746mg

Colorful Chicken Casserole

Preparation Time: 14 minutes

Cooking Time: 14 minutes

Servings: 6

Ingredients:

- 1 cup broth, chicken
- 3 cups cooked chicken, diced
- 4 cups chopped broccoli
- 1 cup assorted colored bell peppers, chopped
- 1 cup cream
- 4 T sherry
- ¼ c hand-shredded Parmesan cheese
- 1 small size can black olives, sliced, drained
- 2 Tortilla Factory low-carb whole wheat tortillas
- ½ c hand-shredded mozzarella

Directions:

1. Place broccoli and chicken broth into a skillet.

2. Top with lid, bring to a boil, and steam until desired crispness. (4 min)

41

3. Add the peppers, steam for one minute if you don't want them crisp.

4. Add the chicken and stir to heat.

5. Combine the sherry, cream, parmesan, and olives.

6. Tear the tortillas into bite-sized pieces.

7. Stir into the chicken and broccoli.

8. Pour cream sauce over the chicken, stir.

9. Top with hand-shredded mozzarella.

10. Broil in oven until cheese is melted and golden brown.

Nutrition: Calories: 412 Total Fat: 30g Protein: 29 Total Carbs: 10g Dietary Fiber: 9g Sugar: 1g Sodium: 712mg

Chicken Relleno Casserole

Preparation Time: 19 minutes

Cooking Time: 29 minutes

Servings: 6

Ingredients:

- 6 Tortilla Factory low-carb whole wheat tortillas, torn into small pieces
- 1 ½ cups hand-shredded cheese, Mexican
- 1 beaten egg
- 1 cup milk
- 2 cups cooked chicken, shredded
- 1 can Ro-tel
- ½ cup salsa Verde

Directions:

1. Grease an 8 x 8 glass baking dish
2. Heat oven to 375 degrees
3. Combine everything together, but reserve ½ cup of the cheese
4. Bake it for 29 minutes

5. Take it out of oven and add ½ cup cheese

6. Broil for about 2 minutes to melt the cheese

Nutrition: Calories: 265 Total Fat: 16g Protein: 20g Total Carbs: 18g Dietary Fiber: 10g Sugar: 0g Sodium: 708mg

Italian Chicken with Asparagus and Artichoke Hearts

Preparation Time: 9 minutes

Cooking Time: 40 minutes

Servings: 1

Ingredients:

- 1 can long asparagus spears, drained
- 1 c red peppers, roasted, drained
- 1 c artichoke hearts, drained
- 6 oz. of boneless chicken breast, pounded thin or sliced thinly
- 2 T parmesan cheese
- 1 T Bisquick
- ½ tsp oregano
- ½ tsp garlic powder
- ½ cup fresh sliced mushrooms
- 2 T red wine vinegar
- 2 T butter
- 3 T olive oil

Directions:

1. Place in a small blender container (or bowl) the oregano, garlic powder, vinegar, and 1 T oil. Place to the side.

2. Combine the Bisquick and Parmesan cheese.

3. Roll the chicken in the Bisquick and Parmesan mix.

4. Heat the butter in a skillet.

5. Brown the chicken on both sides and cook until done, approximately 4 minutes.

6. Emulsify or quickly whip the wet ingredients you have placed to the side. This is your dressing.

7. Place the chicken on the plate.

8. Surround with the vegetables and drizzle them with the dressing.

Nutrition: Calories: 435 Total Fat: 18g Protein: 38g Total Carbs: 16g Dietary Fiber: 7g Sugar: 1g Sodium: 860mg

SIDE DISHES

Brussels Sprouts Delight

Preparation time: 10 minutes

Cooking time: 8 minutes

Servings: 4

Ingredients:

- 2 tablespoons olive oil
- 2 garlic cloves, minced
- 2 tablespoons coconut aminos
- and ½ pounds Brussels sprouts, halved
- ounces water
- and ½ teaspoon white pepper

Directions:

1. Put the oil in your instant pot, add garlic, Brussels sprouts, aminos, water and white pepper, stir, cover and cook on High for 8 minutes.
2. Divide among plates and serve as a side dish.
3. Enjoy!

Nutrition: Calories 162, fat 2, fiber 1, carbs 2, protein 5

Special Sweet Potatoes

Preparation time: 10 minutes

Cooking time: 10 minutes

Servings: 8

Ingredients:

- cup water
- tablespoon lemon peel, grated
- tablespoons stevia
- A pinch of sea salt
- sweet potatoes, peeled and sliced
- ¼ cup ghee
- ¼ cup maple syrup
- cup pecans, chopped
- tablespoon arrowroot powder
- Whole pecans for garnish

Directions:

1. Pour the water in your instant pot, add lemon peel, stevia, sweet potatoes and salt, stir, cover, cook on High for 10 minutes and transfer them to a plate.
2. Set your instant pot on Sauté mode, add the ghee and heat it up
3. Add pecans, maple syrup arrowroot powder, stir very well and cook for 1 minutes,

4. Divide sweet potatoes between plates, drizzle the pecans sauce all over, top with whole pecans and serve.
5. Enjoy!

Nutrition: Calories 162, fat 2, fiber 1, carbs 5, protein 6

MEATS RECIPES

Portobello Mushrooms with Sausage and Cheese

Preparation time: 10 minutes

Cooking time: 20 minutes

Servings: 2

Ingredients:

- 2 Portobello mushroom caps
- 2 oz sausage
- tbsp melted butter, unsalted
- tbsp grated parmesan cheese
- 1/8 tsp garlic powder
- 1/8 tsp red chili powder
- ¼ tsp salt
- tsp avocado oil

Directions:

1. Turn on the oven, then set it to 425 degrees F and let it preheat.
2. Meanwhile, remove the stems from mushroom caps, chop them and then brush the caps with butter inside-out.

3. Take a frying pan, place it over medium heat, add oil and when hot, add sausage, crumble it, sprinkle with garlic powder and then cook for 5 minutes until cooked.
4. Stir in mushroom stems, season with salt and black pepper, continue cooking for 3 minutes until cooked and then remove the pan from heat.
5. Distribute sausage-mushroom mixture into mushroom caps, sprinkle cheese, and red chili powder on top and then bake for 10 t0 12 minutes until mushroom caps have turned tender and cooked. Serve.

Nutrition: 310 Calories; 26 g Fats; 10.7 g Protein; 6.6 g Net Carb; 1.1 g Fiber;

Sausage and Cauliflower Rice

Preparation time: 5 minutes

Cooking time: 15 minutes;

Servings: 2

Ingredients:

- 7 oz grated cauliflower
- 3 oz sausage
- green onion, sliced
- ½ tsp garlic powder
- tbsp avocado oil
- 1/3 tsp salt
- ¼ tsp ground black pepper
- 6 tbsp water

Directions:

1. Take a medium skillet pan, place it over medium heat, add 1 tbsp oil and when hot, add sausage and cook for 4 to 5 minutes until nicely browned.
2. Switch heat to medium-low level, pour in 4 tbsp water and then simmer for 5 to 7 minutes until sausage has thoroughly cooked.
3. Transfer sausage to a bowl, wipe clean the pan, then return it over medium heat, add oil and when hot, add cauliflower rice and green onion, sprinkle with garlic powder, salt, and black pepper.

4. Stir until mixed, drizzle with 2 tbsp water, and cook for 5 minutes until softened.

5. Add sausage, stir until mixed, cook for 1 minute until hot and then serve.

Nutrition: 333 Calories; 31.3 g Fats; 9.1 g Protein; 0.8 g Net Carb; 2.5 g Fiber;

Cheesy Sausage and Egg Bake

Preparation time: 5 minutes

Cooking time: 18 minutes

Servings: 2

Ingredients:

- 4 oz sausage
- egg
- tbsp grated cheddar cheese
- ½ tbsp grated mozzarella cheese
- ½ tbsp grated parmesan cheese
- ¼ tsp salt
- 1/8 tsp ground black pepper
- tsp avocado oil

Directions:

1. Turn on the oven, then set it to 375 degrees F and let it preheat.
2. Meanwhile, take a medium skillet pan, place it over medium heat, add oil and when hot, add sausage and cook for 5 minutes until cooked.
3. Meanwhile, crack the egg in a medium bowl, add salt, black pepper, and cheeses, reserving 1 tbsp cheddar cheese and whisk until mixed.
4. When the sausage has cooked, transfer it to the bowl containing egg batter and stir until combined.

5. Take a baking pan, grease it with oil, pour in sausage mixture, sprinkle remaining cheddar cheese in the top, and then bake for 10 to 12 minutes until cooked.
6. When done, let sausage cool for 5 minutes, then cut it into squares and then serve.

Nutrition: 439 Calories; 38.9 g Fats; 19.7 g Protein; 2.2 g Net Carb; 0 g Fiber;

POULTRY

Chili Lime Chicken with Coleslaw

Preparation time: 35 minutes

Cooking time: 8 minutes

Servings: 2

Ingredients:

- chicken thigh, boneless
- oz coleslaw
- ¼ tsp minced garlic
- ¾ tbsp apple cider vinegar
- ½ of a lime, juiced, zested
- Seasoning:
- ¼ tsp paprika
- ¼ tsp salt
- tbsp avocado oil
- tbsp unsalted butter

Directions:

1. Prepare the marinade and for this, take a medium bowl, add vinegar, oil, garlic, paprika, salt, lime juice, and zest and stir until well mixed.

2. Cut chicken thighs into bite-size pieces, toss until well mixed, and marinate it in the refrigerator for 30 minutes.
3. Then take a skillet pan, place it over medium-high heat, add butter and marinated chicken pieces and cook for 8 minutes until golden brown and thoroughly cooked.
4. Serve chicken with coleslaw.

Nutrition: 157.3 Calories; 12.8 g Fats; 9 g Protein; 1 g Net Carb; 0.5 g Fiber;

Lime Garlic Chicken Thighs

Preparation time: 35 minutes

Cooking time: 15 minutes

Servings: 2

Ingredients:

- 2 boneless chicken thighs, skinless
- ¾ tsp garlic powder
- ½ tsp all-purpose seasoning
- ½ of lime, juiced, zested
- ½ tbsp avocado oil

Directions:

1. Take a medium bowl, place chicken in it, and sprinkle with garlic powder, all-purpose seasoning, and lime zest.
2. Drizzle with lime juice, toss until well coated and let chicken thighs marinate for 30 minutes.
3. Then take a medium skillet pan, place it over medium heat, add oil and when hot, place marinated chicken thighs in it and cook for 5 to 7 minutes per side until thoroughly cooked.
4. Serve.

Nutrition: 260 Calories; 15.6 g Fats; 26.8 g Protein; 1.3 g Net Carb; 0.6 g Fiber;

Bacon Ranch Deviled Eggs

Preparation time: 5 minutes

Cooking time: 0

Servings: 2

Ingredients:

- slice of bacon, chopped, cooked
- 2/3 tsp ranch dressing
- 1/2 tbsp mayonnaise
- 1/3 tsp mustard paste
- eggs, boiled
- Seasoning:
- ¼ tsp paprika

Directions:

1. Peel the boiled eggs, then slice in half lengthwise and transfer egg yolks to a medium bowl by using a spoon.
2. Mash the egg yolk, add remaining ingredients, except for bacon and paprika and stir until well combined.
3. Pipe the egg yolk mixture into egg whites, sprinkle with bacon and paprika, and then serve.

Nutrition: 260 Calories; 24 g Fats; 8.9 g Protein; 0.6 g Net Carb; 0.1 g Fiber;

Deviled Eggs with Mushrooms

Preparation time: 5 minutes

Cooking time: 0

Servings: 2

Ingredients:

- tbsp chopped mushroom
- tsp mayonnaise
- ½ tsp apple cider vinegar
- tsp butter, unsalted
- eggs, boiled
- Seasoning:
- ¼ tsp salt
- 1/8 tsp ground black pepper
- ¼ tsp dried parsley

Directions:

1. Peel the boiled eggs, then slice in half lengthwise and transfer egg yolks to a medium bowl by using a spoon.
2. Mash the egg yolk, add remaining ingredients and stir until well combined.
3. Pipe the egg yolk mixture into egg whites, sprinkle with black pepper, and then serve.

Nutrition: 130.5 Calories; 10.9 g Fats; 7.1 g Protein; 0.6 g Net Carb; 0.1 g Fiber;

SEAFOOD RECIPES

Special Oysters

Preparation Time: 10 minutes

Cooking Time: 0 minutes

Servings: 4

Ingredients:

- 12 oysters; shucked
- Juice of 1 lemon
- 2 tablespoons ketchup
- Serrano chili pepper; chopped.
- Juice from 1 orange
- Zest from 1 orange
- 1/4 cup cilantro; chopped.
- 1/4 cup scallions; chopped.
- Juice from 1 lime
- Zest from 1 lime
- cup tomato juice
- 1/2 teaspoon ginger; grated
- 1/4 cup olive oil
- 1/4 teaspoon garlic; minced
- Salt to the taste.

Directions:

1. In a bowl, mix lemon juice, orange juice, orange zest, lime juice and zest, ketchup, chili pepper, tomato juice, ginger, garlic, oil, scallions, cilantro and salt and stir well.
2. Spoon this into oysters and serve them.

Nutrition: Calories: 100 Fat: 1 Fiber: 0 Carbs: 2 Protein: 5

Octopus Salad

Preparation Time: 10 minutes

Cooking Time: 40 minutes

Servings: 2

Ingredients:

- 21 ounces octopus; rinsed
- Juice of 1 lemon
- 4 celery stalks; chopped.
- 4 tablespoons parsley; chopped.
- 3 ounces olive oil
- Salt and black pepper to the taste.

Directions:

1. Put the octopus in a pot, add water to cover, cover the pot, bring to a boil over medium heat; cook for 40 minutes, drain and leave aside to cool down.
2. Chop octopus and put it in a salad bowl.
3. Add celery stalks, parsley, oil, and lemon juice and toss well.
4. Spice with salt and pepper, toss again and serve

Nutrition: Calories: 140 Fat: 10 Fiber: 3 Carbs: 6 Protein: 23

Irish Style Clams

Preparation Time: 5 minutes

Cooking Time: 15 minutes

Servings: 4

Ingredients:

- 2 pounds clams; scrubbed
- 3 ounces pancetta
- small green apple; chopped.
- thyme springs; chopped.
- tablespoon olive oil
- tablespoons ghee
- garlic cloves; minced
- bottle infused cider
- Juice of 1/2 lemon
- Salt and black pepper to the taste.

Directions:

1. Heat a pan with the oil over medium-high heat; add pancetta, brown for 3 minutes and reduce temperature to medium.
2. Add ghee, garlic, salt, pepper, and shallot; stir and cook for 3 minutes
3. Increase the heat again, add cider; stir well and cook for 1 minute

4. Add clams and thyme, cover the pan and simmer for 5 minutes
5. Discard unopened clams, add lemon juice and apple pieces; stir and divide into bowls. Serve hot.

Nutrition: Calories: 100 Fat: 2 Fiber: 1 Carbs: 1 Protein: 20

Grilled Swordfish

Preparation Time: 10 minutes

Cooking Time: 10 minutes

Servings: 3

Ingredients:

- 4 swordfish steaks
- 3 garlic cloves; minced
- tablespoon parsley; chopped.
- 1/4 cup lemon juice
- lemon; cut into wedges
- 1/3 cup chicken stock
- 1/2 teaspoon marjoram; dried
- tablespoons olive oil
- 1/2 teaspoon rosemary; dried
- 1/2 teaspoon sage; dried
- Salt and black pepper to the taste.

Directions:

1. In a bowl, mix chicken stock with garlic, lemon juice, olive oil, salt, pepper, sage, marjoram, and rosemary and whisk well.
2. Put swordfish steaks, toss to coat and keep in the fridge for 3 hours
3. Place marinated fish steaks on preheated grill over medium-high heat and cook for 5 minutes on each side

4. Arrange on plates, top with parsley, then serve with lemon wedges on the side.

Nutrition: Calories: 136 Fat: 5 Fiber: 0 Carbs: 1 Protein: 20

Salmon Patties

Preparation Time: 5 minutes

Cooking Time: 15 minutes

Servings: 4

Ingredients:

- egg
- 14 oz. canned salmon, drained
- 4 tbsp. intermittent almond flour
- 4 tbsp. cup cornmeal
- 4 tbsp. Onion, minced
- ½ tsp. garlic powder
- tbsp. mayonnaise
- Salt and pepper to taste

Directions:

1. Flake apart the salmon with a fork.
2. Put the flakes in a bowl and combine with the garlic powder, mayonnaise, intermittent almond flour, cornmeal, egg, onion, pepper, and salt.
3. Use your hands to shape equal portions of the mixture into small patties and put each one in the Air Fryer basket.
4. Air fry the salmon patties at 350°F for 15 minutes. Serve hot.

Nutrition: Calories:

Cheese Tilapia

Preparation Time: 10 minutes

Cooking Time: 10 minutes

Servings: 4

Ingredients:

- lb. tilapia fillets
- ¾ cup parmesan cheese, grated
- tbsp. parsley, chopped
- tsp. paprika
- tbsp. olive oil
- Pepper and salt to taste

Directions:

1. Preheat the Air Fryer to 400°F.
2. In a shallow dish, combine the paprika, grated cheese, pepper, salt, and parsley.
3. Puta light drizzle of olive oil at the tilapia fillets. Cover the fillets with the paprika and cheese mixture.
4. Lay the fillets on a sheet of aluminum foil and transfer to the Air Fryer basket. Fry for 10 minutes. Serve hot.

Nutrition: Calories: 246 kcal Protein: 30.12 g Fat: 12.22 g Carbohydrates: 4.35 g

Parmesan Crusted Tilapia

Preparation Time: 10 minutes

Cooking Time: 5 minutes

Servings: 4

Ingredients:

- ¾ cup grated parmesan cheese
- 4 tilapia fillets
- tbsp. olive oil
- tbsp. chopped parsley
- tsp. paprika
- Pinch garlic powder

Directions:

1. Preheat your Air Fryer at 350°F.
2. Coat each of the tilapia fillets with a light brushing of olive oil.
3. Combine all of the other ingredients in a bowl.
4. Cover the fillets with the parmesan mixture.
5. Line the base of a baking dish with a sheet of parchment paper and place the fillets in the dish.
6. Moved to the Air Fryer and cook for 5 minutes. Serve hot.

Nutrition: Calories: 244 kcal Protein: 30.41 g Fat: 12.24 g Carbohydrates: 3.29 g

© 101 - Cooking For Two

Salmon Croquettes

Preparation Time: 8 minutes

Cooking Time: 7 minutes

Servings: 4

Ingredients:

- lb. can red salmon, drained and mashed
- ⅓ cup olive oil
- eggs, beaten
- cup intermittent-friendly bread crumbs
- ½ bunch parsley, chopped

Directions:

1. Preheat the Air Fryer to 400°F.
2. In a mixing bowl, combine the drained salmon, eggs, and parsley.
3. In a shallow dish, stir together the bread crumbs and oil to combine well.
4. Mold equal-sized amounts of the mixture into small balls and coat each one with bread crumbs.
5. Put the croquettes in the fryer's basket and air fry for 7 minutes.

Nutrition: Calories: 442 kcal Protein: 30.48 g Fat: 32.64 g Carbohydrates: 5.31 g

CHUNKY FISH

Preparation Time: 10 minutes

Cooking Time: 8 minutes

Servings: 4

Ingredients:

- 2 cans canned fish
- 2 celery stalks, trimmed and finely chopped
- egg, whisked
- cup intermittent-friendly bread crumbs
- tsp. whole-grain mustard
- ½ tsp. sea salt
- ¼ tsp. freshly cracked black peppercorns
- tsp. paprika

Directions:

1. Combine all of the ingredients in which they appear. Mold the mixture into four equal-sized cakes. Leave to chill in the refrigerator for 50 minutes.
2. Put on an Air Fryer grill pan. Spritz all sides of each cake with cooking spray.
3. Grill at 360°F for 5 minutes. Turn the cakes over and resume cooking for an additional 3 minutes.
4. Serve with mashed potatoes if desired.

Nutrition: Calories: 245 kcal Protein: 40.31 g Fat: 5.67 g Carbohydrates: 5.64 g

VEGETABLES

Chanterelles with Cheddar Cheese

Preparation time: 2 minutes

Cooking time: 8 minutes

Servings: 4

Ingredients:

- tablespoon olive oil
- cloves garlic, minced
- (1-inch) ginger root, grated
- 1/2 teaspoon dried dill weed
- teaspoon dried basil
- 1/2 teaspoon dried thyme
- 16 ounces Chanterelle mushrooms, brushed clean and sliced
- 1/2 cup water
- 1/2 cup tomato purée
- tablespoons dry white wine
- 1/3 teaspoon freshly ground black pepper
- Kosher salt, to taste
- cup Cheddar cheese

Directions:

1. Press the "Sauté" button to heat up the Instant Pot. Then, heat the olive oil; sauté the garlic and grated ginger for 1 minute or until aromatic.
2. Add dried dill, basil, thyme, Chanterelles, water, tomato purée, dry white wine, black pepper, and salt.
3. Secure the lid. Choose "Manual" mode and Low pressure; cook for 5 minutes. Once cooking is complete, use a quick pressure release; carefully remove the lid.
4. Top with shredded cheese and serve immediately. Bon appétit!

Nutrition: 218 Calories; 15.1g Fat; 9.5g Carbs; 9.9g Protein; 2.3g Sugars

Family Cauliflower Soup

Preparation time: 2 minutes

Cooking time: 8 minutes

Servings: 4

Ingredients:

- 4 tablespoons butter, softened
- 1/2 cup leeks, thinly sliced
- 2 cloves garlic, minced
- 3/4 pound cauliflower, broken into florets
- cup water
- cups chicken stock
- cup full-fat milk
- Kosher salt, to taste
- 1/3 teaspoon ground black pepper

Directions:

1. Press the "Sauté" button to heat up your Instant Pot. Then, melt the butter; sauté the leeks until softened.
2. Then, sauté the garlic until fragrant, about 30 seconds. Add the remaining ingredients and gently stir to combine.
3. Secure the lid. Choose "Manual" mode and Low pressure; cook for 5 minutes. Once cooking is complete, use a quick pressure release; carefully remove the lid.

4. Ladle into individual bowls and serve warm. Bon
   appétit!

Nutrition: 167 Calories; 13.7g Fat; 8.7g Carbs; 3.8g Protein; 5.1g
Sugars

Cauliflower and Kohlrabi Mash

Preparation time: 2 minutes

Cooking time: 15 minutes

Servings: 4

Ingredients:

- 1/2 pound cauliflower, cut into florets
- 1/2 pound kohlrabi, peeled and diced
- cup water
- 3/4 cup sour cream
- garlic clove, minced
- Sea salt, to taste
- 1/3 teaspoon ground black pepper
- 1/2 teaspoon cayenne pepper

Directions:

1. Add 1 cup of water and a steamer basket to the bottom of your Instant Pot.
2. Then, arrange cauliflower and kohlrabi in the steamer basket.
3. Secure the lid. Choose "Manual" mode and Low pressure; cook for 3 minutes. Once cooking is complete, use a quick pressure release; carefully remove the lid.
4. Now, puree the cauliflower and kohlrabi with a potato masher. Add the remaining ingredients and stir well. Bon appétit!

Nutrition: 89 Calories; 4.7g Fat; 9.6g Carbs; 3.6g Protein; 2.6g Sugars

Buttery and Garlicky Fennel

Preparation time: 2 minutes

Cooking time: 6 minutes

Servings: 6

Ingredients:

- 1/2 stick butter
- 2 garlic cloves, sliced
- 1/2 teaspoon sea salt
- ½ pounds fennel bulbs, cut into wedges
- 1/4 teaspoon ground black pepper, or more to taste
- 1/2 teaspoon cayenne pepper
- 1/4 teaspoon dried dill weed
- 1/3 cup dry white wine
- 2/3 cup chicken stock

Directions:

1. Press the "Sauté" button to heat up your Instant Pot; now, melt the butter. Cook garlic for 30 seconds, stirring periodically.
2. Add the remaining ingredients.
3. Secure the lid. Choose "Manual" mode and Low pressure; cook for 3 minutes. Once cooking is complete, use a quick pressure release; carefully remove the lid. Bon appétit!

Nutrition: 111 Calories; 7.8g Fat; 8.7g Carbs; 2.1g Protein; 4.7g Sugars

SOUPS AND STEWS

Homemade Cold Gazpacho Soup

Preparation Time: 15 minutes + chilling time

Cooking Time: 0 minutes

Servings: 6

Ingredients:

- 2 small green peppers, roasted
- 2 large red peppers, roasted
- 2 medium avocados, flesh scoped out
- 2 garlic cloves
- 2 spring onions, chopped
- cucumber, chopped
- cup olive oil
- tbsp. lemon juice
- tomatoes, chopped
- 7 ounces goat cheese
- small red onion, chopped
- tbsp. apple cider vinegar
- Salt to taste

Direction:

1. Place the peppers, tomatoes, avocados, red onion, garlic, lemon juice, olive oil, vinegar, and salt, in a food processor. Pulse until your desired consistency is reached. Taste and adjust the seasoning.
2. Transfer the mixture to a pot. Stir in cucumber and spring onions. Cover and chill in the fridge at least 2 hours. Divide the soup between 6 bowls. Serve topped with goat cheese and an extra drizzle of olive oil.

Nutrition: Calories: 528 Fat,: 45.8g Net Carbs: 6.5g Protein: 7.5g

Cream of Thyme Tomato Soup

Preparation Time: 10 minutes

Cooking Time: 15 minutes

Servings: 6

Ingredients:

- 2 tbsp. ghee
- 2 large red onions, diced
- ½ cup raw cashew nuts, diced
- 2 (28 oz) cans tomatoes
- tsp fresh thyme leaves + extra to garnish
- ½ cups water
- Salt and black pepper to taste
- cup heavy cream

Directions:

1. Melt ghee in a pot over medium heat and sauté the onions for 4 minutes until softened.
2. Stir in the tomatoes, thyme, water, cashews, and season with salt and black pepper. Cover and bring to simmer for 10 minutes until thoroughly cooked.
3. Open, turn the heat off, and puree the ingredients with an immersion blender. Adjust to taste and stir in the heavy cream. Spoon into soup bowls and serve.

Nutrition: Calories 310 Fat 27g Net Carbs 3g Protein 11g

Creamy Cauliflower Soup with Bacon Chips

Preparation Time: 10 minutes

Cooking Time: 15 minutes

Servings: 4

Ingredients:

- 2 tbsp. ghee
- onion, chopped
- head cauliflower, cut into florets
- cups water
- Salt and black pepper to taste
- cups almond milk
- cup shredded white cheddar cheese
- bacon strips

Directions:

1. Melt the ghee in a saucepan over medium heat and sauté the onion for 3 minutes until fragrant.
2. Include the cauli florets, sauté for 3 minutes to slightly soften, add the water, and season with salt and black pepper. Bring to a boil, and then reduce the heat to low. Cover and cook for 10 minutes. Puree cauliflower with an immersion blender until the ingredients are evenly combined and stir in the almond milk and cheese until the cheese melts. Adjust taste with salt and black pepper.

3. In a non-stick skillet over high heat, fry the bacon, until crispy. Divide soup between serving bowls, top with crispy bacon, and serve hot.

Nutrition: Calories 402 Fat 37g Net Carbs 6g, Protein 8g

Power Green Soup

Preparation Time: 15 minutes

Cooking Time: 15 minutes

Servings: 6

Ingredients:

- broccoli head, chopped
- cup spinach
- onion, chopped
- garlic cloves, minced
- ½ cup watercress
- 5 cups veggie stock
- cup coconut milk
- tbsp. ghee
- bay leaf
- Salt and black pepper, to taste

Directions:

1. Melt the ghee in a large pot over medium heat. Add onion and garlic, and cook for 3 minutes. Add broccoli and cook for an additional 5 minutes. Pour the stock over and add the bay leaf. Close the lid, bring to a boil, and reduce the heat. Simmer for about 3 minutes.
2. At the end, add spinach and watercress, and cook for 3 more minutes. Stir in the coconut cream, salt and black

pepper. Discard the bay leaf, and blend the soup with a hand blender.

Nutrition: Calories: 392 Fat,: 37.6g Net Carbs: 5.8g Protein: 4.9g

SNACKS

Bacon Ranch Fat Bombs

Preparation time: 15 minutes

Cooking time: 15 minutes

Servings: 4

Ingredients:

- 8 oz full-fat cream cheese, softened
- tbsp ranch dressing dry mix
- slices bacon

Directions:

1. Preheat the oven to 375°F.
2. Cook the bacon strips on a baking tray for 15 minutes. Let cool, then crumble.
3. In a bowl, add cream cheese and sprinkle with ranch dressing dry mix. Stir in the bacon. Mix thoroughly.
4. Form a ball out of 1 tbsp of the mixture. Repeat to form 3 more bombs. Refrigerate for 2 hours. Serve.

Nutrition: Total Carbs – 9.5 g Net Carbs – 2.7 g Fat – 38.9 g Protein – 11.4 g Calories – 419

Salmon Mascarpone Balls

Preparation time: 7 minutes

Cooking time: 0

Servings: 6

Ingredients:

- 3 oz smoked salmon, chopped
- 3 oz mascarpone
- ½ tsp maple flavor
- ½ tsp chives, chopped
- 3 Tbsp hemp hearts

Directions:

1. In a small food processor, combine salmon, mascarpone, maple flavor, and chives. Pulse a few times until blended together.
2. Form mixture into 6 balls.
3. Put hemp hearts on a medium plate and roll individual balls through to coat evenly.
4. Serve immediately or refrigerate up to 3 days.

Nutrition: Total Carbs – 1 g Net Carbs – 0 g Fat – 5 g Protein – 3 g Calories – 65

Bacon, Artichoke & Onion Fat Bombs

Preparation time: 15 minutes

Cooking time: 8 minutes

Servings: 4

Ingredients:

- 2 bacon slices
- 2 tbsp ghee
- ½ large onion, peeled, diced
- garlic clove, minced
- ⅓ cup canned artichoke hearts, sliced
- ¼ cup sour cream
- ¼cup mayonnaise
- tbsp lemon juice
- ¼ cup Swiss cheese, grated
- Salt, pepper to taste
- 4 avocado halves, pitted

Directions:

1. In a hot skillet, fry the bacon for 5 minutes. Let cool, then crumble.
2. Cook the onion and garlic using ghee for 3 minutes.
3. Combine the onion and garlic with the bacon and the remaining ingredients. Mix well. Season with salt and pepper. Refrigerate 30 minutes. Fill the avocado halves with the mixture and serve.

Nutrition: Total Carbs – 10 g Net Carbs – 4 g Fat – 39.6 g Protein – 6.6 g Calories – 408

SMOOTHIES AND DRINKS

Vanilla Intermittent Smoothie

Preparation Time: 11 minutes

Cooking Time: 0 minutes

Servings: 1

Ingredients:

- 13.5-oz (400ml) can coconut milk
- cup heavy cream
- 1/4 cup sweetener or to taste
- tsp vanilla extract
- cups ice cubes

Directions:

1. Put all together the ingredients in a blender and blend until pureed.

Nutrition: 379 calories 38g fat 4g carbohydrates 3g protein

DESSERTS

Mocha Ice Cream

Preparation time: 2 hours and 5 minutes

Cooking time: 0

Servings: 2

Ingredients:

- cup coconut milk
- ¼ cup heavy whipping cream
- tbsp erythritol
- 15 drops liquid stevia
- tbsp unsweetened cocoa powder
- tbsp instant coffee
- ¼ tsp xanthan gum

Directions:

1. Whisk everything except xanthan gum in a bowl using a hand mixer.
2. Slowly add xanthan gum and stir well to make a thick mixture.
3. Churn the mixture in an ice cream machine as per the machine's instructions.

4. Freeze it for 2 hours then garnish with mint and instant coffee.
5. Serve.

Nutrition: Calories 267 Total Fat 44.5 g Saturated Fat 17.4 g Cholesterol 153 mg Sodium 217 mg Total Carbs 8.4 g Sugar 2.3 g Fiber 1.3 g Protein 3.1 g

Strawberry Ice Cream

Preparation time: 2 hours and 5 minutes

Cooking time: 0

Servings: 6

Ingredients:

- cup heavy whipping cream
- 1/3 cup erythritol
- large egg yolks
- ½ tsp vanilla extract
- 1/8 tsp xanthan gum
- tbsp vodka
- cup strawberries, pureed

Directions:

1. Add cream to a pot and place it over low heat and warm it up.
2. Stir in 1/3 cup erythritol and mix well to dissolve.
3. Beat in egg yolks and continue whisking until fluffy.
4. Stir in vanilla extract and mix well until smooth.
5. Lastly, add 1/8 tsp xanthan gum and the vodka.
6. Mix well then transfer the mixture to an ice cream machine and churn as per the machine's instructions.
7. Freeze it for 1 hour then add pureed strawberries.
8. Churn again and freeze for another 1 hour.
9. Serve.

Nutrition: Calories 259   Total Fat 34 g Saturated Fat 10.3 g Cholesterol 112 mg Sodium 92 mg Total Carbs 8.5 g Sugar 2 g Fiber 1.3 g Protein 7.5 g

Intermittent Vanilla Ice Cream

Preparation time: 8 hours and 5 minutes

Cooking time: 0

Servings: 8

Ingredients:

- 2 15-oz cans coconut milk
- 2 cup heavy cream
- ¼ cup Swerve confectioner's sweetener
- tsp pure vanilla extract
- Pinch kosher salt

Directions:

1. Refrigerate coconut milk for 3 hours or overnight and remove the cream from the top while leaving the liquid in the can. Place the cream in a bowl.
2. Beat the coconut cream using a hand mixer until it forms peaks.
3. Stir in vanilla, sweeteners, and whipped cream then beat well until fluffy.
4. Freeze this mixture for 5 hours.
5. Enjoy.

Nutrition: Calories 255 Total Fat 23.4 g Saturated Fat 11.7 g Cholesterol 135 mg Sodium 112 mg Total Carbs 2.5 g Sugar 12.5 g Fiber 1 g Protein 7.9 g

CPSIA information can be obtained
at www.ICGtesting.com
Printed in the USA
BVHW092054190421
605311BV00002B/36